THE FOREST ISSUE

INTO THE WOODS WE GO

Walking to the Kishorn Islands

by Katriona Chapman

Scottish Highlands, Winter 2010

I walk into the forest, fast, to keep warm.

after a while I leave behind the last human footprints

Otters!

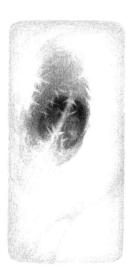

I feel animals all around me but I'm noisy in the snow and they stay out of sight.

My destination.
This view.

The deepest silence, broken only by trickling water and birds.

I listen for a long time, sun on my face

Then I turn back.

ANGUS RUADGH

STORY + SOME WORDS ADAPTED FROM DAVID THOMSON'S "THE PEOPLE OF THE SEA", 1954

"I COME FROM A MAN THAT HAS MONEY IF YOU CAN GET HIM A HUNDRED SEALSKINS" THE STRANGER SAID. "YOU MUST TALK WITH HIM THIS NIGHT."

"VERY WELL."

THEY TOOK THE ROAD SO FAST THAT THE WIND THAT WAS IN THE BACK OF THEM COULD NOT KEEP PACE WITH THEM.

THEY CAME TO A CLIFF THAT OVER-HUNG THE SEA 400 FEET BELOW.

"ARE WE GONE ASTRAY?" SAYS ANGUS. "NO, WE ARE HERE."
"AND WHERE IS THE MAN YOU SPOKE OF?" ASKED ANGUS.
THE STRANGER STOOD CLOSE BEFORE HIM AND SAID: "YOU'LL SEE."

THE STRANGER TOOK ANGUS IN HIS ARMS WITH A STRONG GRIP AND PRESSED HIS BODY CLOSE TO HIM AND BLEW A LONG BREATH DOWN INTO HIS MOUTH. AND THE STRANGER LIFTED ANGUS AND DIVED WITH HIM DOWN INTO THE SEA.

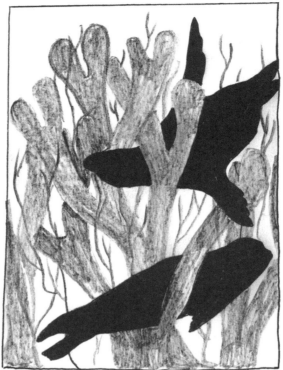

DEEP DOWN AND INTO A FOREST OF KELP AND BLADDERWRACK. THE STRANGER LED HIM THROUGH PAST A GREAT MANY ROOMS OF FOLK WAILING AND CRYING. ANGUS PRAYED MERCY FOR HIS LIFE.

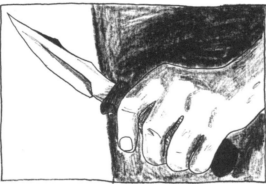

"ANGUS RUADGH, DID YOU EVER SEE THIS KNIFE BEFORE?" SAYS THE STRANGER. "I DID. IT'S MY OWN KNIFE THAT I LOST THIS DAY HUNTING. I STUCK THAT KNIFE INTO A SEAL, AND THE SEAL ESCAPED WITH IT INTO THE WATER". "THAT SEAL WAS MY FATHER." SAID THE STRANGER.

IT'S ONLY YOU THAT CAN CURE HIM ANGUS. YOU MUST CLOSE THE WOUND WITH YOUR OWN HAND.

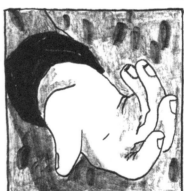

"THANK YOU ANGUS." SAID THE STRANGER, "NOW IF YOU WILL MAKE AN OATH BEFORE US NOW NEVER TO KILL OR HARM ANOTHER SEAL FOR AS LONG AS YOU LIVE, I WILL TAKE YOU BACK TO THE LAND WHERE YOU LIVE." ANGUS SWORE A SOLEMN OATH.

ANGUS DID NEVER SEE THAT STRANGER AGAIN, BUT HE KEPT HIS OATH.
AND SOME FEW TIMES WHEN THINGS WERE TIGHT, AND ANGUS MISSED HIS TRADE, HE'D FIND GIFTS AT HIS DOOR.

ALEXANDRA HIGLETT

R. Lemstra 2022

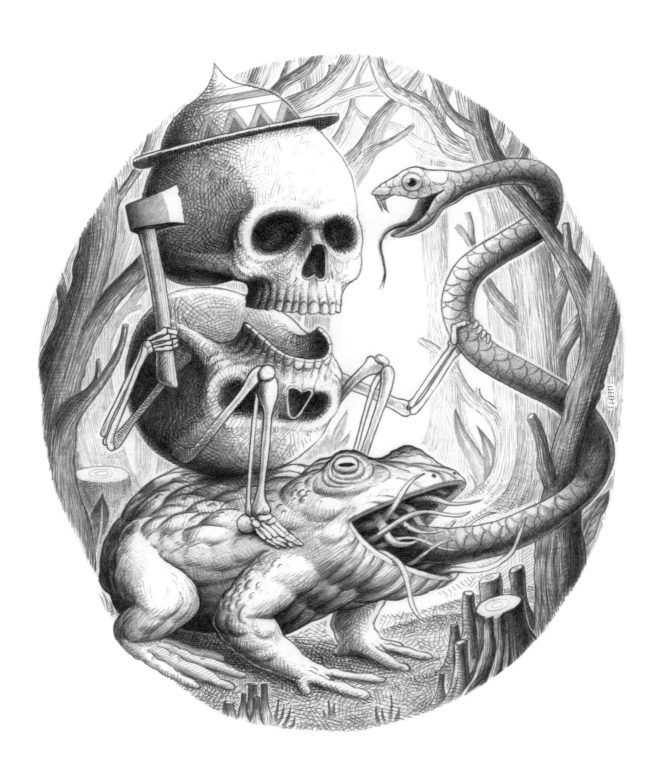

THERE WAS A BIGGISH KIND OF WOOD BEHIND MY GRANDPARENTS' HOUSE. THE ROOM MY BROTHER AND I WOULD SLEEP IN DURING THE HOLIDAYS LOOKED RIGHT OUT ONTO IT.

IT SEEMED TOO GOOD TO BE TRUE, THIS WILD PLACE BEING SO CLOSE AND ACCESSIBLE. MY PARENTS DIDN'T KNOW BUT I WAS ALLOWED TO WALK IN THERE ON MY OWN AND MY IMAGINATION FLOURISHED.

IT WAS ALWAYS DISAPPOINTING WHEN MY GRANDPARENTS HAD NO GHOST STORIES OR STRANGE OCCURRENCES TO REPORT. I WANTED TO HEAR ABOUT MYSTERIOUS LIGHTS OR THE FINDING OF A HUMAN SKULL.

IT DOESN'T GO THAT FAR. THERE'S A WALL AND THEN IT'S JUST PEOPLE'S GARDENS, IT'S ONLY A COPSE.

I REMEMBER MAKING STUFF UP. ONE TIME I TOLD MY BROTHER THAT I'D SEEN A GIANT FACE, PUSHED UP AGAINST THE EDGE OF THE FOREST.

IT WAS STARING RIGHT AT THE HOUSE

NO JOKE?

I SWEAR ON MUM AND DAD'S LIFE

WOOD WIZARD

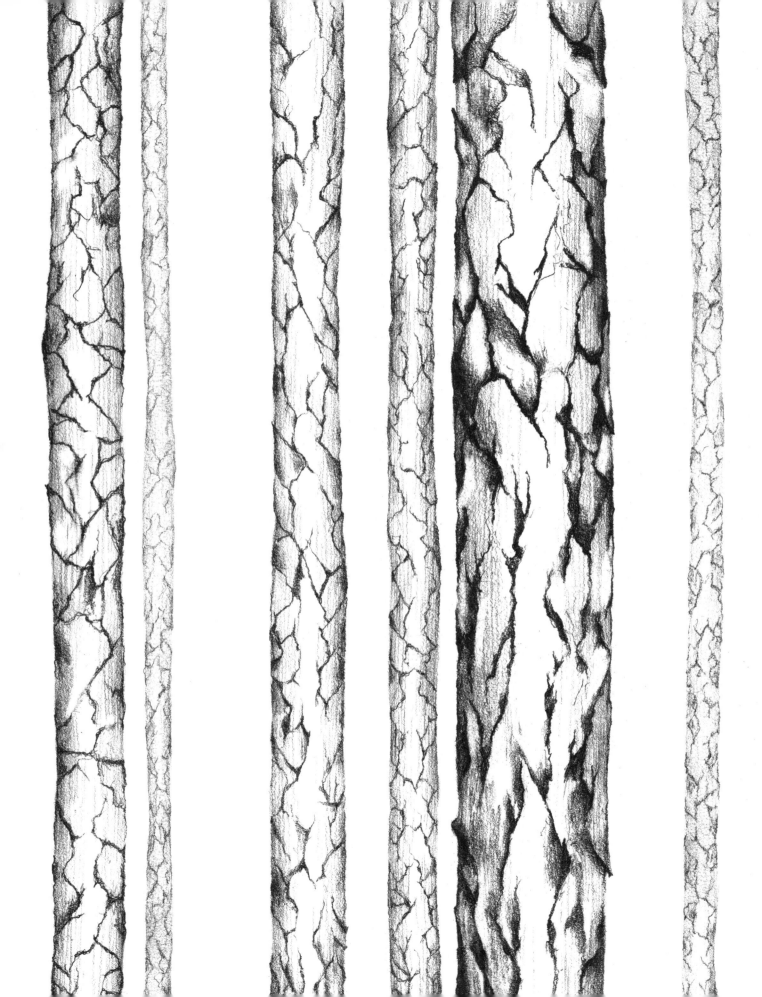

KRISTYNA BACZYNSKI

Kristyna Baczynski is a Leeds-based illustrator, comic artist and designer. She grew up in The Pennines of Yorkshire, to a family from The Carpathians of Ukraine. She also freelances, teaches and self-publishes books and zines.

www.kristyna.co.uk // @kbaczynski

VANESSA FOLEY

Vanessa Foley is a painter/pencil artist based in Newcastle. She loves wildlife and getting out into the countryside. She has exhibited widely and is currently collaborating with the clothing label Stand Tall Amongst Giants.

www.vanessafoley.co.uk // @vanessafoleyart

RACHEL M. BRAY

Rachel M. Bray is a Canadian artist who loves to work with graphite. She is inspired by archeology, anthropology and biology. She has exhibited widely, but also likes finding unusual & new venues for her art.

www.rachelmbray.com // @rachelmbray

CAITLIN HACKETT

Caitlin Hackett is a Brooklyn-based artist who grew up on the Northern coast of California surrounded by nature. She creates pseudo-mythical, mutated, and anthropomorphic creatures, and specialises in ballpoint pen.

www.caitlinhackett.carbonmade.com // @Caitlin_Hackett

KATRIONA CHAPMAN

Katriona Chapman is a London-based illustrator and comic artist who's worked for clients such as Oxford University Press and HarperCollins. She prints handmade zines and books under the name 'Tomatito Press.'

www.katrionachapman.com // @katchapman

ALEXANDRA HIGLETT

Alexandra Higlett is a UK-based illustrator and designer. She graduated from Falmouth's MA programme in Authorial Illustration and runs Pirrip Press, a design and print studio specialising in silkscreen/letterpress printing.

www.alexhiglett.com // www.pirrippress.co.uk

SANDRA DIECKMANN

London-based illustrator working with clients such as Random House & Atomic Skis. In 2011, Sandra was chosen by Oscar-winning illustrator Shaun Tan as the "Emerging Talent Winner" at the Cheltenham Illustration Awards.

www.sandradieckmann.com // @sandradieckmann

AMBER HSU

Amber Hsu is a Chinese-born, US-raised, UK-based artist, writer, and designer. She was selected as a *3x3 Illustration Annual* winner in 2012, and is also a maker of artzines and other ephemera, including *Tiny Pencil*.

www.hsubili.com // @amberhsu

LISA EVANS

Lisa Evans is an illustrator based in Bath in the UK. She has an MA in Children's Book Illustration from Cambridge School of Art, and has worked with clients such as Templar Publishing, Chronicle Books & Mojo.

www.firefluff.com // @firefluff

JOHN D. KILBURN

John D. Kilburn is an illustrator and designer based in Cornwall. His clients include Atlantic Press Books, Falmouth University and Slut clothing. He also sells handmade pop-up books, zines & silkscreen prints.

www.johndkilburn.com // *@JohnDKilburn*

LUKE PEARSON

Luke Pearson is a cartoonist / illustrator / comics type person from the UK. He is best known for his *Hilda* series of comics and *Everything We Miss*, both published by Nobrow Press.

www.lukepearson.com // *@thatlukeperson*

RAYMOND LEMSTRA

Raymond Lemstra is an Amsterdam-based artist who exhibits all over the world. He is often inspired by primitive art and is interested in conveying a sense of child-like awe with his fantastical images.

www.raymondlemstra.nl // *@RaymondLemstra*

CHRIS RIXON

Chris Rixon is an artist/illustrator based in the South-West of England. He usually specialises in pen & ink, and has an MA in Illustration: Authorial Practice from University College, Falmouth. He exhibits widely.

www.crixonillustration.com

JON MACNAIR

Jon MacNair is a Portland-based illustrator who has exhibited world-wide. His work has also appeared in various editorial publications and various package and apparel designs.

www.jonmacnair.com // *@jlmacnair*

SIGRID RØDLI

Sigrid Rødli is a Norwegian illustrator who has studied illustration in both Norway and the UK. She is especially fond of illustrating subject-matter relating to nature, fantasy and fairy tales.

www.cargocollective.com/sigridrodli

JAMIE MILLS

Jamie Mills is a UK-based illustrator with a first class degree in illustration. He exhibits throughout the UK and creates beautiful self-published art books which he sells at www.etsy.com/shop/JamieMilk

www.jamie-mills.co.uk // *@jamiemilk*

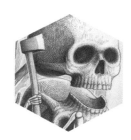

NICK SHEEHY

Nick Sheehy is an Australian-born artist and illustrator living in the south-east of England. He has worked with Nickelodeon, Nobrow Press, Pictoplasma and Cartoon Network amongst many others.

www.showchicken.com // *@showchicken*

ALLISON SOMMERS

Allison Sommers is a Brooklyn-based art-worker working in gouache and mixed media. She creates complicated, intricate, uncomfortable worlds of viscera and beasts, and exhibits world-wide.

www.allisonsommers.com // *@allison_sommers*

RIMA STAINES

Rima Staines is a UK-based artist who is interested in folklore, wilderness and nomadic living. Along with pencil she also uses paint, wood, word, music, animation, clock-making and puppetry to tell her stories.

www.intothehermitage.blogspot.co.uk //
@thehermitage

DONYA TODD

Donya Todd is an illustrator, painter and comic artist who lives on a farm in Cornwall. She takes her inspiration from the magical, marvellous and macabre, and works with clients such as Foyles, Samsung & The Independent.

www.donyatodd.co.uk // @Donyatodd

LIAM STEVENS

Liam Stevens is London-based image maker and designer. He favours simple materials enabling him to craft his work through expressive lines or graphic shapes. Clients include the New Statesman & Condé Nast.

*www.liamstevens.com // @Liam_Stevens_*

SARAH TSE

Sarah Tse is a New York based Chinese artist graduated from Central Saint Martins. Her nostalgic, fantasy-themed drawings are paradoxes inspired by her travels and dreams. Sarah has exhibited in New York, London, and many parts of Asia.

www.sarahtse.com // @sarahtse1216

LIZZY STEWART

Lizzy Stewart is a London-based illustrator inspired by folk culture, musicand the places in which she finds herself. She has been published by the Folio Society, Faber & Faber and the Guardian.

www.abouttoday.co.uk // @lizzystewart

STUART WHITTON

Stuart Whitton is a Welsh illustrator based in London. He loves traditional media, and uses pencil to create meticulously hand-drawn illustrations which have been published and exhibited internationally.

www.stuartwhitton.co.uk // @stuartwhitton

YOKO TANAKA

Yoko Tanaka is an award-winning painter and graduate of the Art Center College of Design in Pasadena. Now based in the UK, she has exhibited worldwide and also illustrated a number of books, including The Magician's Elephant by Kate DiCamillo.

www.yokotanaka.com

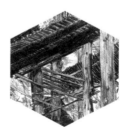

WARD ZWART

Ward Zwart is an illustrator based in Antwerp, Belgium. He has exhibited around the world and created and contributed to numerous zines. He has also worked with the Flemish Opera, Nobrow Press and Vice Magazine.

www.cargocollective.com/wardzwart

JACK TEAGLE

Jack Teagle is an illustrator based in South West England. He keeps many sketchbooks and goes through many tubes of paint. He has worked with clients such as Converse, Nobrow Press and Anorak Magazine.

www.jackteagle.co.uk // @jackteagle

TINY EMPIRE PRESS • LONDON

TINY PENCIL
THE FOREST ISSUE

Tiny Pencil is published by the Tiny Empire Press. Printed in the UK on FSC certified paper by The Lavenham Press.

Please visit www.tinypencil.com for further information or to place an order. ISBN: 978-1-909743-00-7.

Front Cover Art by Nick Sheehy. Back cover illustrations by Kristyna Baczynski.
Forest detail preceding contributor pages by Katriona Chapman. Incidental insects by Amber Hsu.

TINY PENCIL is Designed and Directed by Amber Hsu and Katriona Chapman.

GIVING GOOD GRAPHITE AND CARBON COPY SINCE 2013.